The Earth's climate system

Figure 2 gives an impression of our climate system in action. The Earth's atmosphere, oceans, and icecaps are all part of the system. Set in constant motion by the Sun's energy, like some gigantic engine, these components interact to produce our daily weather and longer-term climate. Scientists are now using information collected by satellites – on, for example, cloud cover, ocean surface temperature and extent of ice and snow – as well as conventional meteorological data, in their efforts to understand the working of the system. Powerful computers are greatly assisting scientists in this task. However, the immense complexity of our climate system means that the goal of this approach, a model of our climate realistic enough to provide a basis for long term forecasts, must remain a dream for the future.

Exploring the climates of the past

Fortunately there is another approach towards understanding climate change. It consists of exploring the climates of the past. Past weather and climate information lies hidden, not only in old documents, but also in trees and lake beds, polar icecaps and deep ocean muds, to mention only a few of Nature's climate records. Scientists and scholars with a wide range of backgrounds are studying these records. They are gradually piecing together the story of how the Earth's climate has varied in the past (fig 1), and are beginning to understand why it has done so.

This review gives a brief account of how this type of research is carried out, what has already been found, and what it means, both for our own immediate future and for the long term prospects for our civilisation.

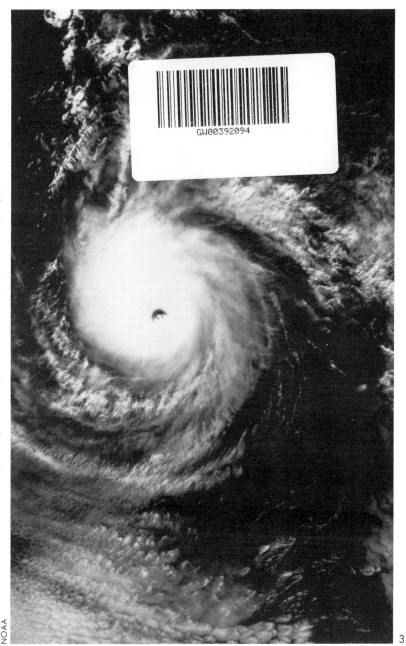

NOAA

3

4 Account roll for the manor of Hendon, refers to a great drought in the summer of 1340.

5 Account roll for the manor of Knightsbridge mentions a drought in the summer of 1342.

Old documents

Official records of temperature, barometric pressure, and rainfall have been kept for less than a century in most parts of the world. Although significant climate changes have taken place within this period we need access to a much longer record if we are to acquire any real understanding of the behaviour of our climate. Important steps in this direction are taking place, in particular, at the Climatic Research Unit at the University of East Anglia. Here, in one project, use is being made of the earliest 18th and 19th century European temperature and pressure records to produce series of daily and monthly weather maps for these periods.

Thermometers and barometers first became available in the mid-17th century, and enthusiasts started to include readings made with these instruments in their weather diaries. Professor Gordon Manley has used a number of such early weather journals to compile a series of mean monthly temperatures for central England going back to 1659. This temperature series, the longest of its kind in the world, records an episode of intense cold in the late 17th century (fig 1). This episode appears to have marked the climax of the so-called Little Ice Age, a longer period during which glaciers advanced in many parts of the world.

Because farming activities depend so much on the weather, much climate information may be gleaned from old farm records. For example, the number of lambs that die at lambing time depends on the severity of the spring, and the amounts of seed per acre required for spring and autumn sowing depend on the wetness of these seasons. A wealth of details of this kind is contained in English manorial account rolls of the 13th and 14th centuries. Studies of account rolls belonging to the bishopric of Winchester and the Abbey of Westminster have increased our knowledge of the climate of medieval England. Indirect evidence is often supported by direct references to weather, mentioned to account for extra items of expenditure. For example, an account roll for the manor of Knightsbridge in Westminster Abbey Library (fig 5), mentions that an extra 30 shillings had

THE SCIENCE MUSEUM

EXPLORING
Our Changing Climate

Tom Williamson BA MSc

LONDON HER MAJESTY'S STATIONERY OFFICE

The Sun's heating is greatest at the equator. Here, warm moist air rises, forms clouds, and moves towards the poles

South Pole

Ice sheets cool the Earth by reflecting away warming sunlight

Winds and ocean currents transport heat from the equator towards the poles

NASA

2

2 This photograph from space, taken during the Southern Hemisphere summer, provides a striking overall view of the Earth's climate system in action.

3 Evaporation due to intense solar heating of tropical waters spawns huge storms like this typhoon, photographed by the NOAA-2 weather satellite in 1973.

Why study climate change?

Eighteen thousand years ago much of Britain lay buried beneath vast sheets of ice, hundreds of metres thick. Ever since this astonishing fact was discovered in the last century scientists have speculated on the nature of the Ice Age climate and the changes that brought it to an end.

More recently, people have wondered if climate changes could be taking place in our own time. During the early 1970s there were disastrous droughts in Africa and frequent failures of the Indian monsoon. In 1976 Britain sweltered in the hottest summer for over a century and experienced one of the worst droughts since records began. By contrast, the following autumn was one of the wettest on record. Could such events as these be the symptoms of a worldwide climate shift?

Even small changes in climate can have a highly damaging effect on agriculture. With grain reserves now standing at only a few percent of annual production, the world is highly vulnerable to adverse shifts in climate. An understanding of how and why climate changes take place has never been more urgently needed.

been needed to pay for iron for two ploughs and shoes for two cart-horses and four plough-horses, because of the great drought in the summer of 1342. Ploughshares and horseshoes wear out more quickly during droughts, when the soil is hard and dry.

The harsh continental climate of north China is quite different from the gentle climate of the British Isles, kept mild in winter by the warming waters of the Gulf Stream. But in understanding worldwide climate change, records of past climates in China are as useful as those of Western Europe. During the last decades of the 19th century, farmers near Anyang in north China unearthed strangely marked 'bones' when tilling their fields. These 'dragon bones' were sold locally for medicinal use. Scholars soon recognised the markings to be an archaic Chinese script and, by 1904, were able to read the bones. The bones, mainly fragments of sheeps' shoulder blades and turtle shells, were found to date from later part of the Shang dynasty, around 1400 to 1100 BC. They were used in a curious method of divining. After posing a question, often asking if it would rain on a certain day, heat was applied to a small chiselled out cavity in the bone. The resulting pattern of cracks was interpreted as the reply of the oracle. Questions, prayers, and sometimes the results of prayers were recorded on the oracle bones. Studies of those inscriptions referring to rain (fig 6) have lead to a striking conclusion. During Shang times, rain was the commonest form of winter precipitation in the Anyang area, whereas today it is snow. Winters in north China must then have been appreciably milder than they are now. This fits in with other evidence of a long period of worldwide warmth, that was interrupted by a cold interval about 3000 years ago.

6 The inscription on this 3000 year old Chinese oracle bone asks whether it will rain on a certain day. The symbols for rain are encircled. Such inscriptions provide evidence on the climate of ancient China.

Wine harvests & cherry blossom

Ripening of fruit depends on the weather during the growing season, which, in climates like those of Western Europe, is the spring to autumn period each year during which soil temperatures remain above about 6°C. Fruit harvest records can thus provide valuable information on spring and summer temperatures.

In French wine-producing regions local communities used to appoint committees of expert 'judges of the ripeness of the grape' to fix the day each year when the grapes were considered ready for gathering. These annual dates were recorded in local registers and pronouncements, many of which survive in municipal archives. Using such records, French historians have compiled series of annual wine harvest dates, extending back to the 14th century. The 18th and 19th century dates in this series correlate well with instrumentally recorded temperatures; the warmer the spring and summer temperature, the earlier the wine harvest. Calibrated in this way the wine harvest 'thermometer' provides a valuable guide to European spring and summer temperatures in the centuries before instrumental records began.

In Germany, where wine harvest dates are not available, records of wine quality provide a more approximate guide to local temperatures. 'Extra gut' wines imply warm, dry springs and summers, conversely 'sauer' wines suggest cold, wet growing seasons.

Another, more general, climatic deduction may be made from historical wine growing evidence. During the 11th to 13th centuries, large vineyards were widespread in Southern England and Belgium, where springs and summers are now usually too cool and cloudy for large-scale commercial wine growing. From such evidence, Professor Hubert Lamb, of the Climatic Research Unit, infers that between 1100 and 1300 AD summer temperatures in Central England were about 0·7°C above their 1900-1950 average.

To build up a picture of how the global climate has varied through the centuries, climate records from as many parts of the world as possible need to be identified

BRITISH LIBRARY

7

Records of annual wine harvest dates in France provide information on how spring and summer temperatures have varied since medieval times.

These woodcuts from Livre des Prouffitz Champestres, 1529, by Petrus de Crescentiis, show:

7 Pruning the vine
8 Gathering grapes
9 Treading grapes
10 Cleaning casks

8

and assembled. The following Japanese examples illustrate two types of evidence that may be used.

A party was traditionally held at Kyoto as soon as the cherry trees *Prunus yedoensis* were in full bloom. Records of the dates of the annual party extend back from the 19th to the 9th centuries AD. Because the flowers bloomed earlier in mild springs, the dates of the parties provide a useful record of spring temperatures in central Japan.

Lake Suwa, also in central Japan, usually freezes over in winter; the colder the winter, the earlier it freezes. Local priests noted the date each year when the lake froze over; this series of dates goes back to the 15th century and provides a record of winter temperatures in the area.

These Japanese records, supported by similar data from China, suggest that historical climate changes in the Far East have not coincided with those experienced in Europe. Thus, although the 17th century was cold in China and Japan, as in Europe, the 12th century, apparently mild in Europe, was cold in the Far East.

To decide which record, European or Oriental, is more representative of the behaviour of the global climate we need to examine the climate records of trees and other natural objects. Because they do not depend on human recording, these natural records can provide us with climate information from all parts of the world, not only those that possess a documentary heritage.

To be of use to the climatologist, a natural process must generate climate information that is both accessible and datable. The ideal record would consist of a long continuous series of yearly layers. Each layer would possess some measurable property, whose variation with time would correspond precisely to that of temperature or rainfall. Some of Nature's records approach this ideal surprisingly closely.

10

9

Trees

It is well known that the age of a tree may be found by counting the number of its annual growth rings. The 'rings' are sections of cylindrical growth layers, laid down each year during the growing season on the inside of the bark. Annual rings are usually only clearly displayed by trees growing in climates with noticeable seasonal fluctuations. The seasonal variation may be one of temperature, as in Britain, or rainfall, as in many tropical countries. Tree-rings possess a number of measurable properties such as ring width, wood isotope composition, and wood density; which record yearly changes in climate.

A year of low temperature or rainfall can retard the growth of a tree, causing it to form an unusually narrow ring. A narrow ring produced by a tree living in the Arctic or high on a mountain, where temperature is the main growth-limiting factor, indicates a cold growing season. However, when a tree living in a climate where low rainfall is the main limit to growth produces a narrow ring, a dry year is indicated. In Britain, narrow rings usually indicate years of drought.

As a tree grows, each year's new wood is manufactured by photosynthesis from rainwater and carbon dioxide. A tiny fraction of the oxygen and hydrogen atoms in rainwater are heavier than normal, and the proportion of these heavier isotopes depends on the temperature. This isotopic proportion is preserved in each year's new layer of wood, and may be measured with a mass spectrometer. This method can be used to obtain information on the way local temperatures have varied during the lifetime of a tree.

Wood density, measured by placing a thin wood sliver on film and exposing it to X-rays, also varies with the climate. Density variations within an annual ring can even provide separate information on particular months during the growing season.

Wood isotope and density studies, still in their infancy, may prove particularly useful in the analysis of tree-ring records in countries, like Britain, where ring-widths are not very sensitive to climate variations.

How scientists use tree-rings to study past weather.

11 A thin core is extracted from a tree.

12 Widths of the separate annual rings are measured by examining the core under a binocular microscope fitted with a special eyepiece. Although ring-widths respond to climate changes in a complex way, in Britain narrow rings usually indicate years of drought.

Varying proportions of different pollen grains in lake sediments record changes in vegetation and climate. These pictures were taken with a scanning electron microscope.

13 *Plantago lanceolata* L. (Plantain) Magnified 1760 times.

14 *Quercus robur* L. (Oak) Magnified 2520 times.

Each tree therefore can, under favourable conditions, 'remember' the climate changes that took place within its lifetime. But we require longer climate records than can be provided by a single tree. Most trees live for no more than a few hundred years. Even the bristlecone pines of the American West (fig 22), the world's oldest living things, are no more than 4600 years old, about a millionth of the age of the Earth. Fortunately, the records of living trees can be cross-matched with those of nearby dead trees, in the form of stumps or building timbers, to build up a long, combined record. The records of living and dead cold-sensitive bristlecone pines, high in the White Mountains of California, have been combined to give a temperature record running from 3551 BC to 1950 AD. This tells us, as do the European records, of a 12th to 13th century warm period followed by a longer 'Little Ice Age'. It also records a cold period beginning about 3000 years ago, which ties up with evidence of glacial advance in Alaska at the same time.

Growth-ring analysis is not the only application of the record of trees to the study of past climates. In common with other plants, each species of tree, when in flower, sheds quantities of its own distinctive pollen grains. These tiny grains (figs 13, 14), are dispersed by the wind. Some are carried into lakes or bogs, where they accumulate together with the lake sediment or bog peat. The relative proportions of different pollen grains in the accumulating deposit reflect the composition of local vegetation, which in turn is strongly influenced by the climate.

Unlike tree-rings, which record annual changes in climate, pollen sequences only record climate changes that last for hundreds of years or more. However, they enable us to explore much further back into the past. European pollen sequences, dated by the Carbon-14 method, record the broad sweep of climate history since the end of the last Ice Age. They tell of a strange short-lived re-advance of the ice between 10,000 and 11,000 years ago, followed by a long warm period when oak forests predominated in northwest Europe, where mean temperatures were more than 1°C above those of today.

BRITISH MUSEUM (NATURAL HISTORY)

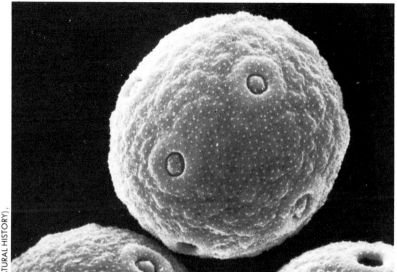

13

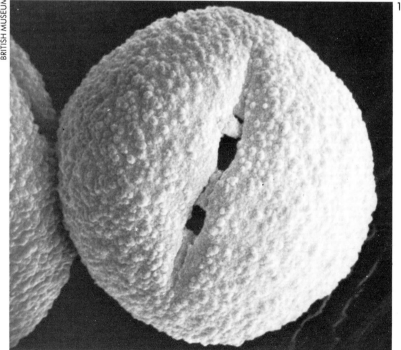

14

E L LADURIE

(a)

(b)

15 According to an engraving made in the 1850s (a), this valley glacier in the French Alps was then close to the village of Argentière; by 1966 (b), the glacier had retreated almost out of sight.

Ice

Ice gives us several sorts of climate information. Signs of the former presence of massive ice sheets in countries such as Britain that now have a mild, temperate climate, provide irrefutable evidence of great changes in temperature (figs. 16, 17). At the height of the last Ice Age about 18,000 years ago temperatures in Britain must have been at least 10°C below those of today.

Evidence of the advance and retreat of mountain glaciers is a sensitive guide to temperature and snowfall changes in the area. Old engravings (fig 15) show that during the 17th, 18th and 19th centuries Alpine glaciers reached much further down their valleys than they do today. Dating by the Carbon-14 method of old moraines (piles of debris deposited by melting ice at the feet of glaciers) shows that glaciers in Alaska, Greenland, and New Zealand, were also much advanced during this 'Little Ice Age'. However, even during the coldest part of this period, world temperatures seem to have been only about 0·5° to 0·8°C lower than those of today. The Little Ice Age was thus in no way comparable with the last real Ice Age.

The great icecaps of Antarctica and Greenland have been built up by the yearly accumulation of snow over millions of years. The layers of snow that turn into ice as they are compressed by the weight of overlying layers, record the temperature in exactly the same way as do the annual growth layers of trees. The lower the temperature, the lower also is the proportion of heavy oxygen (oxygen-18) in the snow when it falls. The record of heavy oxygen in a series of ice layers is thus at the same time a record of temperature. To find out how polar temperature have varied in the past, ice cores have been obtained by drilling deep into the Greenland and Antarctic icecaps. Ice cores are flown to specially equipped laboratories where the heavy oxygen can be measured. As annual layering is seldom visible in the ice, dating of the cores is a problem. One method of dating relies on the fact that, because it forms at higher temperatures, summer snow contains more heavy oxygen than winter snow, producing an annual oscillation in the heavy oxygen record. By counting the number of oscillations downwards from the surface, the age of a particular layer can then be found.

Using this method of dating, work on ice cores up to 400 metres long from the Greenland ice sheet suggests that temperature changes there during the last 2000 years have not corresponded with those in Europe. Clearly much more evidence of this type needs to be collected before we can understand the detailed behaviour of the world's climate during historical times.

The annual heavy oxygen oscillation method of dating is impracticable for longer ice cores. In these cases the age of an ice layer has to be estimated from its depth below the surface. Using this method, the heavy oxygen variations in two ice cores, each more than 1 kilometre in length, obtained by drilling right through the Greenland and Antarctic icecaps, have yielded valuable records of polar temperature changes during the last Ice Age (see fig 29).

Ice contains yet another meteorological record. The proportion of trapped air in a layer of ice at depth records the air pressure at the surface of the icecap when the layer of ice was formed. Because air pressure varies inversely with height above sea-level, tiny trapped air bubbles in ice can tell us how thick the polar icecaps were in the past. Apparently during the last Ice Age, the Greenland icecap, in contrast to the East Antarctic one, which has remained much the same size, was considerably thicker than it is now. So part of the reason why the surface of the Greenland icecap was so much colder during the last Ice Age was simply that it was higher above sea-level. This illustrates the caution that is needed when drawing climatic conclusions from Nature's records.

16 This huge block of sandstone was carried by ice to this site in Northumberland during the last Ice Age. When the ice melted, the block remained behind, oddly perched like this.

17 This U-shaped valley in Dumfriesshire was smoothed by a glacier during the last Ice Age, when Scotland would have looked like parts of Antarctica do today.

18 This Antarctic view is of the Worcester Range in the Transantarctic Mountains, with the Mulock glacier on the left.

17

18

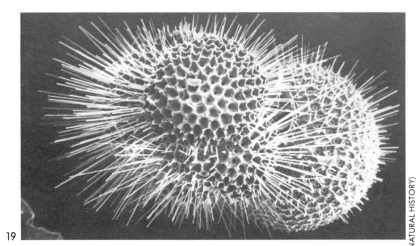

19

20

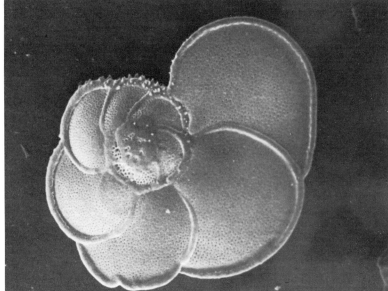

Shells of tiny sea-animals like these are used to study past ocean temperatures. The pictures, magnified about 100 times, were taken with a scanning electron microscope.

19 *Globigerinoides sacculifera*

20 *Globorotalia menardii*

BRITISH MUSEUM (NATURAL HISTORY)

Shells

Ocean waters cover two thirds of the surface area of our planet. Their capacity for absorbing and storing the Sun's heat is crucial to the working of our climate system. Ocean currents also play an important part in transporting heat from the equator towards the poles.

Knowledge of how ocean temperatures have varied in the past is thus of great value to climatologists. Surface temperatures, whose variations are intimately linked with changes in climate, are more useful than deep ocean temperatures, which vary little over thousands of years.

Myriads of tiny shelled animals and plants, of many different species, live in the surface layers of the ocean. When they die, the shells settle towards the bottom. Although the chalky shells dissolve in the cold water at the greatest ocean depths, they remain intact where the ocean floor is shallower. Here the shells accumulate to form a continuous record of temperatures in the surface waters where their former owner-occupiers once lived.

The shells record the temperature in two ways. The first depends on the fact that whereas some species can only live in warm water, others tolerate colder conditions. The relative numbers of different species at any locality are thus related to the local temperature. The second shell 'thermometer' relies on the principle that in a growing shell the proportion of heavy oxygen also depends on the temperature.

These shells accumulate very slowly on the ocean bed. It may take 1000 years to form a layer 1 centimetre thick, the thinnest that can conveniently be sampled and analysed. So the shells' record is of little use for examining short-term climate changes. Conversely, the slowness and continuity of deep sea sedimentation make it ideal for studying the Earth's climate history on time scales of thousands and millions of years. The layers of sediment can be dated using the Carbon-14 method and other techniques involving radioactive decay.

Cores of deep sea sediment, tens of metres in length, are relatively easy to collect. Thousands of such cores

Colour plates

In order to piece together the history of our changing climate, scientists need to consider a bewildering variety of lines of evidence. These include both human documents relating to natural events (fig 21) and Nature's own climate records (fig 22). Such evidence tells of great changes: 50 million years ago Britain's climate was tropical (fig 23), but 18,000 years ago, thick ice sheets covered the northern part of the country (fig 24). In historical times a long cool interval affected Europe from the 14th to the 19th centuries (fig 25). The coldest periods of this 'Little Ice Age' had disastrous consequences for agriculture in Scandinavia and Iceland.

BRITISH LIBRARY

21 Records of the annual date of blossoming of cherry trees in Japan provide evidence of historical climate changes in the Far East. (18th century print by Torii Kiyonaga).

(13)

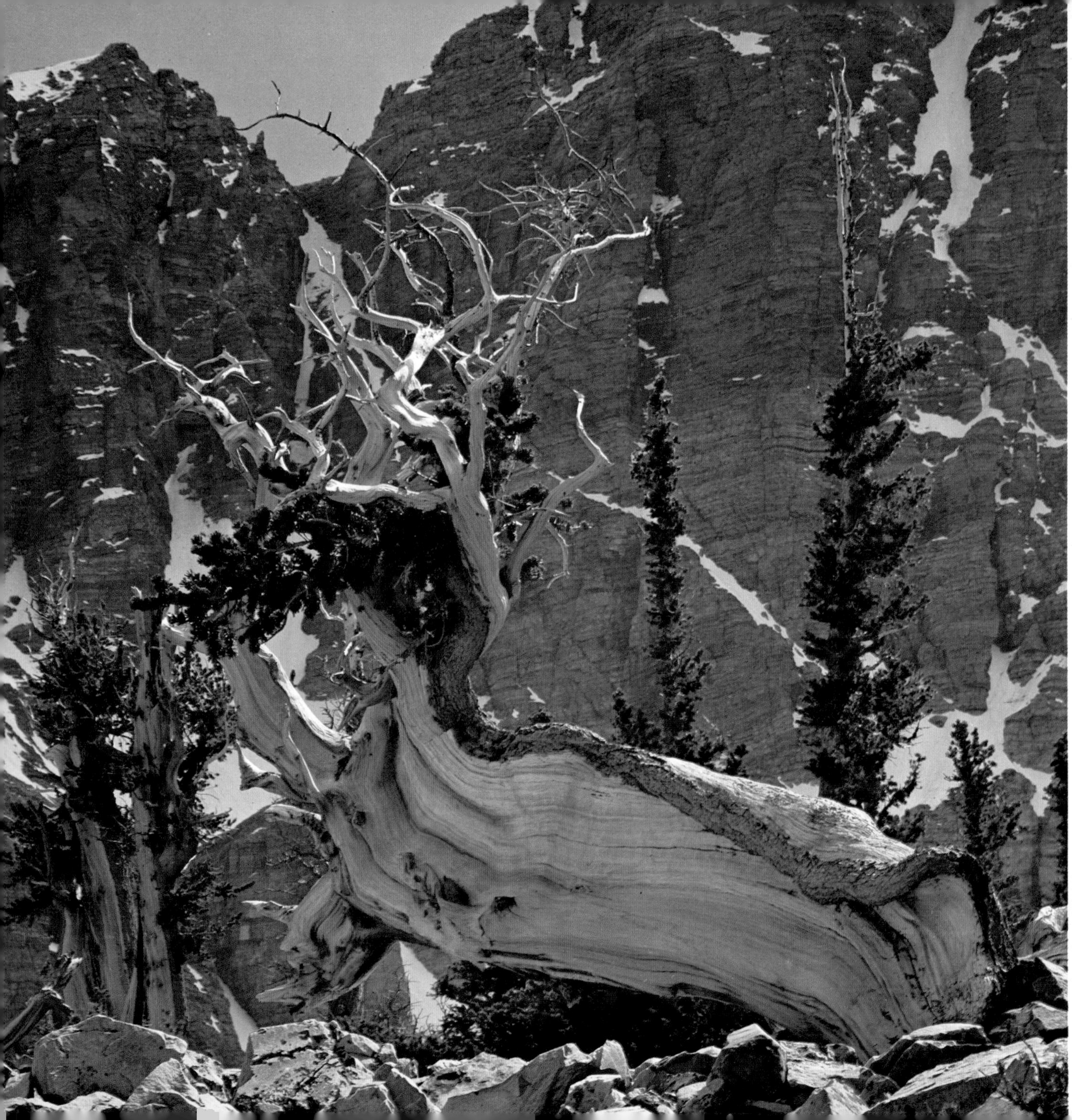

PICTOR INTERNATIONAL

IGS

23

24

IGS

23 An artist's impression of the tropical flora and fauna of the London area 50 million years ago.

24 An impression of a scene in the north of England during the last Ice Age.

opposite page
22 Annual growth-rings of ancient bristlecone pines in the western United States record more than 5000 years of climate change.

25 By the early 15th century, Europe was already entering a long period of generally cooler climates that last until the 19th century. (February, *Très Riches Heures du Duc de Berry*; detail).

from all over the world are currently being studied in the international CLIMAP (Climate Long range Investigation Mapping And Prediction) project. The strategy is to produce a series of climate snapshots of the Earth at significant moments in the past. The first map in the series, one of worldwide ocean surface temperatures at the height of the last Ice Age 18,000 years ago, is already available.

To investigate past ocean temperatures on time scales of millions of years sediment cores hundreds of metres long are needed. During recent years many such long cores have been obtained from the floor of the Southern Ocean in the course of the Deep Sea Drilling Project, another international effort. The heavy oxygen temperature record of the shells in these cores has greatly increased our understanding of the Earth's 50,000,000 year-long cooling trend (fig 1).

We have so far assumed that the shells' heavy oxygen record is one of temperature alone. In fact, it is also influenced by the changing amount of ice in the world. During Ice Ages, a significant fraction of ocean water is locked up in the form of continental ice. This ice contains a smaller proportion of heavy oxygen than seawater does. During icy periods, therefore, both the water that remains in the sea and the shells of the animals that live in it contain a higher proportion of heavy oxygen than they do when the world has little or no ice.

The shells that show this effect most clearly are those of animals that live on the ocean floor. Here, temperatures can have changed little since the northern ice sheets first formed a few million years ago. So the heavy oxygen record of these shells is one of changing global ice volume rather than varying local temperature. However, records of bottom-dwelling shells are not so easy to obtain as those of surface-dwellers, which also record ice volume changes, though less clearly. Ice volume changes in the last 2,000,000 years have been inferred by Nicholas Shackleton of Cambridge University from the heavy oxygen record of a near-surface species (fig 19) living in the equatorial Pacific. These ice volume changes give an impression of the behaviour of our climate during the last 1,000,000 years (fig 1).

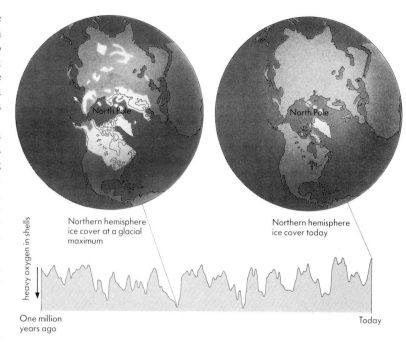

Northern hemisphere ice cover at a glacial maximum

Northern hemisphere ice cover today

heavy oxygen in shells

One million years ago

Today

26 According to the record of heavy oxygen in shells on the ocean floor, there have been repeated fluctuations in the amounts of ice on the northern continents during the last million years.

27

28

27 The conspicuous curve seen in this excavation in Ayrshire marks the upper windward slope of a 200 million year old sand dune. Britain was then a Sahara-like desert.

28 This coal seam in Derbyshire originated about 300 million years ago, when much of Britain was an equatorial swamp.

Rocks

To explore our climate past on the longest time scales we must turn to the rocks of the Earth's crust. Many rocks have been formed by the compaction and hardening of sediments, originally deposited in shallow seas, river deltas, swamps, desert basins, ice margins, and many other environments. By recording their depositional environments, these sedimentary rocks tell us something of the geography and climate of their day. For example, plant remains in the 50,000,000 year old London Clay formation suggest that the local climate was then much warmer and more humid than it is now. Two hundred million-year-old fossil sand dunes, (fig 27) found in many parts of Britain, indicate that desert conditions were widespread at that time.

About 300,000,000 years ago, when the coal seams (fig 28) of the Carboniferous System were laid down, much of Britain, Europe, and North America must have been occupied by tropical swamps. In striking contrast, many rocks of the same age from South Africa, South America and Australia were once moraines, deposited at the margins of vast continental ice sheets. Such a distribution of climates is clearly impossible with the continents and poles of rotation in their present positions. This climatic anomaly was one of the main arguments adduced by the supporters of continental drift, when the idea that our present continents are dispersed fragments of an ancient super-continent, Pangaea, was still a controversial hypothesis. Measurements of fossil magnetism have now established continental drift as a fact, and have enabled continental movements since the formation of Pangaea about 250,000,000 years ago to be traced in some detail. This knowledge provides a framework within which the evidence of rocks from different parts of the world can be fitted, to give us a picture of global climate change during the last 250,000,000 years.

The story of our climate

We have seen how many and how diverse are Nature's records of past climates. But how can we be sure that they really do record worldwide changes in climate? Figure 29 compares five such records from different parts of the world for the last 135,000 years. Their similarity confirms that, on this time scale at least, shells and pollen grains, ice layers and coral terraces truly record global changes in climate. No other factor could link these diverse and scattered records in this way.

As we explore further back into the past, the 'resolution' of each climate record decreases. Tree-rings and short ice cores, which take us back only a few thousand years, respond to yearly weather variation. On the other hand, shells and pollen grains, with records going back hundreds of thousands of years and more, only record those climate changes that last for centuries or millenia. Figure 1, which presents what we know of climate changes during the last 100,000,000 years, illustrates this point. Short term climate fluctuations, such as the 20th century warm period, are not recorded on time scales of millions of years. Nevertheless, fluctuations of this type must have taken place throughout the Earth's history in the same way as they have during the last thousand years.

The view of the past embodied in figure 1, is forced upon us by the nature of the climate records themselves. However, it has an incidental bonus. It shows how our present climate is the outcome of fluctuations taking place on all time scales. Thus both the 50,000,000 year long cooling trend and the warming since the 17th century have, together with many other fluctuations, contributed to the present state of our climate.

Because the past is thus the key both to the present and the future, an understanding of our climate's history is of practical as well as academic value. The following brief account, which attempts to extend and elucidate figure 1, assumes a time perspective similar to that used in the diagram. Starting 4,600,000,000 years ago, when the Earth was formed, the account will become increasingly detailed as we approach the present.

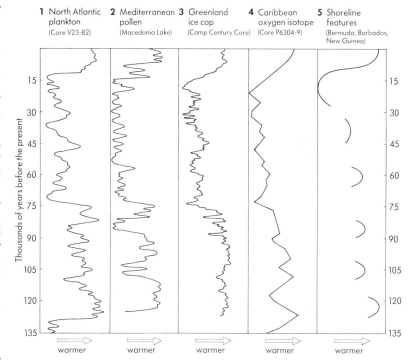

| 1 North Atlantic plankton (Core V23-82) | 2 Mediterranean pollen (Macedonia Lake) | 3 Greenland ice cap (Camp Century Core) | 4 Caribbean oxygen isotope (Core P6304-9) | 5 Shoreline features (Bermuda, Barbados, New Guinea) |

Thousands of years before the present

29 This diagram compares five of Nature's climate records for the last 135,000 years. Their resemblance is good evidence that much of the climate variation on this time scale has been worldwide.

(diagram: US ACADEMY OF SCIENCES)

Record 1 is based on the proportions of different species of shell in a deep sea core west of Ireland.

Record 2 shows the changing proportions of tree pollen in sediment at the bottom of a lake in Yugoslavia.

Record 3 is a heavy oxygen record from a long ice core in Greenland.

Record 4 is a heavy oxygen record provided by shells in a deep sea core from the Caribbean.

Record 5 shows changes in sea-level recorded in Barbados, Bermuda, New Guinea, and other parts of the world.

(19)

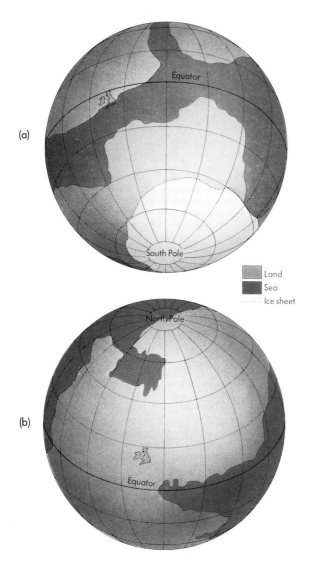

(a)

South Pole

Land
Sea
----- Ice sheet

(b)

North Pole

Equator

30 (a) 300 million years ago Britain lay near the equator and had a moist tropical climate. By contrast, South America, South Africa, and Australia formed part of a large continent that extended over the South Pole and was partly covered by thick ice sheets.

(b) 200 million years ago, Britain lay in the interior of a supercontinent, out of reach of moisture-bearing sea winds, and was a Sahara-like desert. (see fig 27).

Although little is known about the very early climate history of the Earth, average world temperatures cannot have varied beyond limits tolerable to living things (perhaps ranging from 5°C to 35°C) since life emerged sometime before 3,000,000,000 years ago.

There was no oxygen in the early atmosphere. However, about 1,000,000,000 years ago, reddened, oxidised rocks were laid down in different parts of the world. By this time, apparently, sufficient oxygen had been released into the atmosphere as a by-product of photosynthesis by early plants to oxidise the iron in sediments to its familiar rusty colour.

Ultraviolet rays from the Sun can convert oxygen to ozone, a gas whose molecules consist of three oxygen atoms rather than the two of normal oxygen. This process produced a layer of ozone in the upper atmosphere. By shielding the Earth's surface from the Sun's lethal ultraviolet rays, this ozone layer enabled living things to colonise the land surface, until then a barren desert. By about 400,000,000 years ago, green carpets of vegetation had spread across the continents. The consequent changes in reflectivity and water-retaining properties of land surfaces must have marked a major step in the evolution of our climate.

We have already seen how, according to the rocks, 300,000,000 years ago, when much of Britain was an equatorial swamp, South Africa was overwhelmed by ice. The configuration of continents at that time (fig 30a), deduced from measurements of fossil magnetism, explains this climate evidence and supports the assumption that the Earth then had a system of climate zones similar to that of the present day.

Two hundred million years ago the continents had assembled into one supercontinent, Pangaea (fig 30b). Much of the interior of this vast landmass was out of reach of moisture-bearing sea winds, and desert conditions became widespread (fig 27). By about 100,000,000 years ago the supercontinent had disintegrated. Broad seaways between the new continents allowed moisture-bearing winds to penetrate far inland. Fifty million years ago tropical rainforests covered much of the land surface of this equable, wet Earth.

By now the continued dispersal of the continents had left Australia and South America attached to Antarctica, which was already sited over the South Pole. Then South America and Australia separated from Antarctica, leaving this continent cold and isolated, out of reach of warming ocean currents (fig 31). By about 25,000,000 years ago, enough snow had piled up on the cooling Antarctic continent to form a thick ice cap. This ice must have helped to cool the Earth further, by reflecting away warming sunlight. Continued continental motions pushed North America and Eurasia into their present positions, encircling the North Pole in a pincerlike movement. Three million years ago, as our ancestors were evolving from their ape-like forebears, the Earth had cooled enough for thick ice sheets to build up on these northern lands as well as on Antarctica.

Because the northern continents are nearer to the equator than Antarctica is, ice and snow there melts more readily in the summer sun than does Antarctic ice. Slow periodic changes in the direction and tilt of the Earth's axis, and the elliptical shape of its orbit, cause the warming effects of sunlight falling on the Northern Hemisphere to vary cyclically over thousands of years. Many times during the last 3,000,000 years, the Sun's heating seems to have been strong enough to melt most of the northern ice. But for much of the time these heating effects were feebler, allowing the ice sheets to reform and persist. Immense ice sheets, the largest centred in Canada and Scandinavia, built up, only to melt again, on about twenty separate occasions during the last 3,000,000 years (fig 1).

At times of maximum ice extent the glaciers sometimes reached as far south as London (52°N). In North America the ice reached much farther south, as far as Kansas City (39°N). Although on the occasion of its last advance, about 18,000 years ago, the British ice reached no further south than the Midlands. Scotland was smothered by 1 kilometre of ice, and must have looked like parts of Antarctica today (fig 18).

The lowering of world sea-levels, due to the locking up as continental ice of up to four percent of ocean water, is a feature of Ice Ages that has long been appreciated. At the last glacial maximum, sea-levels were about 100 metres lower than they are today. South of the ice, Britain was joined to Europe by dry land, and experienced a dry continental climate. On these cold

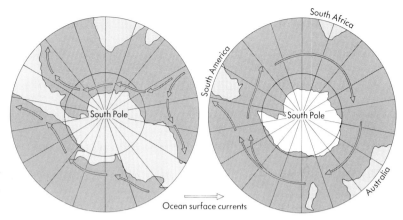

Ocean surface currents

31 Before 50 million years ago (left), Australia and South America were attached to Antarctica. Then South America and Australia broke away, leaving Antarctica cold and isolated, out of reach of warming ocean currents (right). Snow and ice collected by the cooling continent may have helped to cool the whole Earth by reflecting away more of the Sun's energy.

32 An impression of what the Hampshire basin may have looked like 50 million years ago. Tropical rainforests then covered much of the Earth's land surface, extending as far north as Britain.

NATURE

(21)

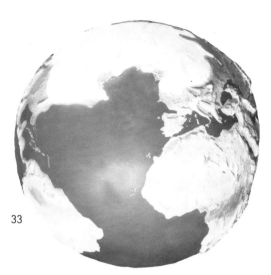

33

33 The world 18,000 years ago, at the height of the last Ice Age. Vast ice sheets, spreading out from centres in Canada, Greenland, Scandinavia and the British Isles, covered much of the northern continents. The tropics were then drier than today, and savannah vegetation covered large areas of equatorial Africa and South America, now occupied by tropical rainforest.

34 The world today. Of the major Northern Hemisphere ice sheets of 18,000 years ago only a shrunken Greenland icecap remains. Water released by melting of the ice sheets has flooded low lying land areas, for example cutting off part of Northwest Europe to form the British Isles.

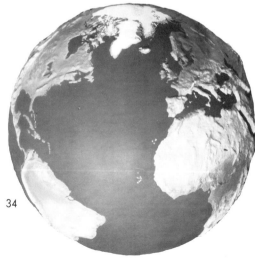

34

northern plains, our ancestors made their living by hunting reindeer, bison and mammoth.

It is now becoming clear that ice expansion in high latitudes, spectacular though it was, was only one aspect of the total pattern of global climate variation associated with Ice Ages. There is much evidence from old lake levels that, contrary to earlier views, the last glacial maximum was a time of great aridity in the tropics. At the same time however, as climate zones were squeezed towards the equator, the Mediterranean winter rain zone seems to have reached parts of North Africa and the Middle East that are now dry. These rains replenished supplies of underground water that are still in use today.

Between 18,000 and 10,000 years ago, motions of the Earth's axis conspired to give the Northern Hemisphere more summer sunlight than it had known for about 70,000 years. This was almost certainly the main reason for the retreat of the ice that followed its maximum about 18,000 years ago. As the ice melted away, forests invaded its former strongholds and world sea-levels rose rapidly (fig 29). Eight thousand years ago the world was warmer than it is today.

After reaching a peak between 4000 and 8000 years ago, a long term decline of world temperature set in, though interrupted by periods both of warmth and more intense cold. There was a cooling about 3000 years ago, when bristlecone pines, growing high in the White Mountains of California, formed unusually narrow rings, and glaciers advanced in Alaska. A warm period seems to have assisted the Norsemen in their settlement of Iceland in the 9th, and Greenland in the 10th centuries AD. In England vineyards flourished during the 12th and 13th centuries, when summers appear to have been warmer and sunnier than those of this century.

During the 14th century another cooling started. Sea-ice appeared off the coasts of Iceland, and forced the Norsemen to change their sea-route to Greenland. The cooling made agriculture and stock raising increasingly difficult in these northern lands. By 1540 the Norse colonists in Greenland had all perished.

In the 17th century, glaciers advanced in many parts of the world. An embryonic ice sheet may have started to form in Baffin Island, Canada. In England, the

Thames froze far more often than it had done before, and Frost Fairs were frequently held on the ice. The biggest Frost Fair was held during the winter of 1683-84, one of the severest winters on record. A whole new city of booths and shops arose on the ice (fig 35).

In Europe, at least, the late 17th century was the coldest period in recorded history and with mean temperatures about 1°C below their present levels the growing season in England was several weeks shorter that it is today. This shortening of the growing season had disastrous consequences for agriculture in Norway and Iceland.

What could have caused this period of intense cold in the late 17th century? One intriguing idea that has received recent support proposes that the Sun's output of radiation may have been unusually low during the period between about 1645 and 1715. There are surprisingly few observations of sunspots and aurorae between these years, implying that the Sun was then less active than it is now. A decrease in the intensity of solar radiation reaching the Earth at this time could have lead to the observed sharp fall in temperatures.

The 18th century brought an end to the period of greatest cold, but mean temperatures remained well below their present levels. The warming continued throughout the 19th century, and the first half of this century was one of the warmest periods in history. Expansion of the tropical rain zone brought rainfall to the southern Sahara and gave India more regular monsoon rains. Agriculture flourished worldwide. This warm period seems to have culminated in the 1940s, and since then a general cooling, in the Northern Hemisphere at least, appears to have prevailed.

35 In Europe the late 17th century was the coldest period of the Little Ice Age. The Thames frequently froze over. This print shows the great Frost Fair held during the winter of 1683–84, when a whole new city of booths and shops arose on the ice.

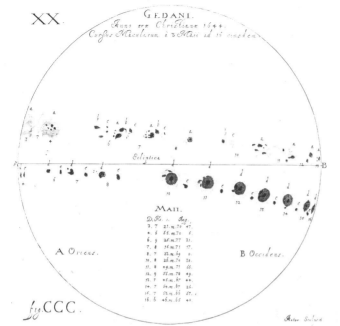

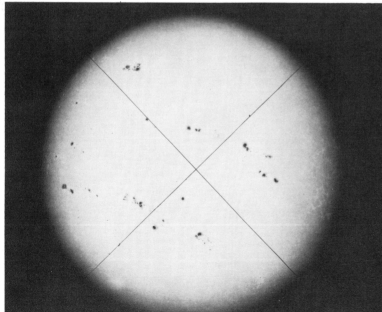

GREENWICH OBSERVATORY

The causes of climate change

We have seen how, by studying both human documents and Nature's records, scientists are gradually building up a picture of how the Earth's climate has varied in the past (fig 1). By enabling us to identify the causes of climate change, such knowledge can help us to understand the vicissitudes of our present climate and to forecast future trends.

Over millions of years, the imperceptible movements of the continents themselves seem to be the most important influences on climate change. Continents are carried around as passengers by the slowly shifting plates that interlock to form the outer, more rigid, part of the Earth. We have already traced the way in which, by isolating the Antarctic continent over the South Pole, plate movements seem to have played a crucial role in the overall cooling of the last 50,000,000 years.

The climate record of the last 1,000,000 years appears to consist of a series of fairly regular fluctuations (fig 1). We have seen how this era of cyclic climate fluctuation began about 3,000,000 years ago, when the global climate had cooled sufficiently for ice sheets to build up on the northern continents, as well as on Antarctica. These fluctuations were attributed to periodic melting of the northern ice, caused by changes in the amounts of sunlight received. The sunlight changes were ascribed to cyclic variations in the direction and tilt of the Earth's axis and in the ellipticity of its orbit around the Sun. Such ideas are associated with a long-standing theory of Ice Ages, known by the name of one of its advocates in the 1920s; Milutin Milankovitch. Until recently the theory had remained unproven. However, in 1976 a group of three scientists, John Imbrie, James Hays, and Nicholas Shackleton, published detailed results of their studies based on the records of shells in cores taken from the bed of the Southern Ocean. They found that both global ice volume and local sea surface temperature varied cyclically. The periods closely matched the 19,000, 23,000, 41,000 and roughly 100,000 year cycles predicted by the Milankovitch theory. This theory is now, therefore, firmly established as the main reason for the comings and goings of the ice during the last 3,000,000 years.

The reasons for the very long term climate changes are thus now, in outline at least, understood. But what about the shorter term fluctuations that have left their imprint on human history? We have already seen how the coldest period of the Little Ice Age may have been caused by a fall in the Sun's output of radiation between 1645 and 1715. There is also a convincing general correlation between inferred variations in solar output and the climate changes of the last 1000 years. This suggests that solar variability may have been one of the most important influences on climate change during historical times.

Another cause of climate change, on shorter time scales at least, could be volcanic activity. Violent volcanic outbursts, such as that of Vesuvius which destroyed Pompeii in 79 AD, shoot immense clouds of gas and dust high into the upper atmosphere. There, sulphur-containing gases react to form tiny droplets of sulphuric acid, which, together with minute silicate dust particles, may be dispersed by the upper winds all over the earth. Such volcanic particles can remain suspended in the upper atmosphere for months or even years. By reducing the intensity of sunlight reaching the surface, these aerosol veils produced by great eruptions can cool the whole earth. In 1815 Tambora, Indonesia, erupted in what was probably by far the greatest volcanic explosion of historical times. It is unlikely to have been a coincidence that the summer of 1816 was, both in Europe and North America, one of the coldest and wettest on record.

The likely causes of climate change discussed so far are all factors outside the Earth's atmosphere-ocean-icecap climate system. But in their effects such external influences are modified by internal rhythms generated by the climate system itself. To determine how much of the total climate variation is self-driven, and how much is due to outside factors of the kind discussed here, is a significant challenge facing climatologists today.

V A SHAMSHIN

37

36 Sunspots, seen in a 1644 sketch by Hevelius and in a 1947 photograph, are a normal feature of the Sun's surface. Very few sunspots were observed between 1645 and 1715; the unusual behaviour of the Sun at this time may have been one of the reasons for the coldness of this period.

37 The immense column of dust and gas produced by the explosion of Bezymianny volcano, Kamchatka, on 30th March 1956, reached a height of more than 36km. Such volcanic clouds become widely dispersed by upper-level winds, and can have worldwide cooling effects.

38 This infra-red heat picture of southern Britain and northern France was taken by satellite on a summer evening. Built-up areas are relatively warm (darker on this image) because they cool more slowly during the evening than the surrounding country.

39 The sharp division clearly seen in this Landsat photograph of part of the Middle East, marks the line of a fence between the pale, overgrazed lands of the Sinai desert (left) and the darker ungrazed lands of the Negev (right). Because of its higher reflectivity, the overgrazed Sinai area is cooler and receives less rainfall than the ungrazed Negev.

What of the future?

Thanks to the records of the past, we now understand something of the causes of climate change, and are in a position to consider what the future may have in store for us.

Neglecting for the moment the effects of Man's activities, the long term future course of our climate can now be predicted. It is a bleak one. Calculations show that amounts of Northern Hemisphere summer sunlight, at present seemingly barely sufficient to keep the ice at bay, will remain low for most of the next 50,000 years. Unless the effects of our own activities on the climate supervene, the sites of many great cities, Berlin, Moscow, Edinburgh and Montreal, will probably, long before the end of this period, be once again buried beneath great thicknesses of ice.

However, important as this knowledge may be for the long-term future of our civilisation, it bears little relevance to the practical difficulties facing 20th century Man. For guidance on likely climate trends during the coming decades and centuries, we must turn to those factors – variations in the Sun's output and in the frequency of great volcanic eruptions – that may be the most important influences on our climate on these shorter time scales. Unfortunately, although a number of scientists are tackling these problems, at present neither the workings of the Sun, nor the complex circumstances that induce volcanoes to erupt at particular times, are sufficiently well understood for reliable predictions to be made.

So far, we have ignored the possible effects of our own activities on the climate. In doing so, we have left out what may in the future become an important factor determining climatic change. By burning fossil fuels such as coal and oil, Man is consuming atmospheric oxygen and replacing it with carbon dioxide. Though transparent to incoming shorter-wave solar radiation, carbon dioxide, together with water vapour, strongly absorbs much of the outgoing longer-wave radiation emitted by the Earth's surface. By trapping the Sun's energy in this way, carbon dioxide helps keep the Earth warmer than it would otherwise be. Since 1850, probably because of deforestation as well as our industrial activities, the amount of carbon dioxide in the atmosphere has increased by about 13 per cent. This extra carbon dioxide may already have had some influence on global climate changes, and by the end of the century its warming effects could become the predominant influence on our climate.

We may also be affecting our climate in other ways. Buildings and roads change the thermal properties of the land surface, and this, together with direct heat from houses, factories, and power stations, already causes warming on a local scale. Central London is probably now on average about 2°C warmer than the surrounding countryside. As world populations and industrial activity increase in the coming decades, urban development and man-made heat could have a worldwide warming effect.

It has already been mentioned that when snow and ice cover a previously vegetation-clad continent, a greater proportion of the Sun's heat is reflected away and cooling may result. The removal of natural vegetation by Man or his grazing animals can have a similar effect on a local scale. Lower rainfall associated with such changes is particularly unfortunate when it occurs in arid regions (fig 39).

In facing the future therefore, we need to understand more fully the effects of our own activities on the climate as well as the causes of those natural climate fluctuations that have influenced the evolution of life and the history of Man. In the meantime, we can draw at least one conclusion of value from the record of past climate fluctuations (fig 1). During the first half of the present century (when defines the climatic 'normal' for most countries) our climate was warmer than the average for the last 1000 years and probably also had less extremes. The surprisingly variable weather of the present period: droughts in the southern Sahara in the early 1970s (fig 40), the European drought and heatwave of 1976, the record-breaking severity of the 1976–77 winter in parts of North America, may thus prove to be less surprising when viewed against the background of the last thousand years. According to this argument, we can expect more such weather in the future.

A PROTO/OXFAM

40 Villagers in Ethiopia dig for water during the 1973 drought, which caused widespread suffering in the countries on the southern fringes of the Sahara. A greater understanding of the processes of global climate change could enable measures to be taken that would lessen the harmful effects of such droughts in the future.

Further reading

Nigel Calder *The Weather Machine* BBC Publications, London, 1974.

E Le Roy Ladurie *Times of Feast, Times of Famine* Allen & Unwin, London, 1972.

John Gribbin *Forecasts, Famines and Freezes* Wildwood House, London, 1976.

Stephen H Schneider *The Genesis Strategy; Climate and Global Survival* Plenum, London, 1976.

MORE TECHNICAL
National Research Council: US Committee for the Global Atmospheric Research Program *Understanding Climatic Change – A Program for Action* National Academy of Sciences, Washington DC, 1975.

H H Lamb *Climate: Present, Past and Future, Volume 1* (Volume 2 due late 1977) Methuen, London, 1972.

The weekly *New Scientist* carries general reviews of recent work in this field. More technical articles appear in *Nature*. The important paper by J D Hays, J Imbrie and N J Shackleton, establishing the presence of Milankovitch cycles in two deep sea cores from the Southern Ocean, was published in *Science* (New York) **194,** 1976, p1121–1132.

Acknowledgements

Many people have helped in the preparation of this booklet. The author is expecially indebted to Professor H H Lamb, Dr T M L Wigley, and Dr H Mörth, of the Climatic Research Unit, University of East Anglia, for critical comments on the manuscript; Dr D V Stern for information on the Westminster Abbey account rolls; Dr N J Shackleton of Cambridge University, Mr D Brett of London University and Mr H A Buckley of the British Museum (Natural History).

Printed in England for Her Majesty's Stationery Office by Raithby, Lawrence & Company Limited at the De Montfort Press: Leicester and London
Dd 587509 K120 9/77

Cover illustration
Sea-ice off the south coast of Greenland. During the 17th, 18th and 19th centuries, sea-ice from the Arctic spread far across the North Atlantic and the colder climate brought misery and famine to the people of Iceland and Scandinavia.